thank you sweet Prince for
all the love and fun no
matter the covid season

ISBN 978-2-9582376-0-8
Written & illustrated by Ari Dalby

Typefaces
Hangyaboly by Roland Huse
Bebus Neue
Benedict
Monument
Arimo

BUBU

Learns to bounce

written & illustrated
by Ari Dalby

The little bulldog was happy to go and visit
Grandpa Papi and Ruth.
He'd never met them before, so it was very
exciting.

Everything was exciting for Bubu.
Everything was new for Bubu!

The English Bulldog pup was a whole five
months old.
He was truly delighted to explore new places,
jump up on new friends and share his joy with
big sloppy kisses.

Grandpa Papi and Ruth greeted Bubu in the front garden with gentle caresses and various compliments.

He heard "friendly fellow", "lovely toffee pudding" "sweet boy" and decided he liked them very much.

It was a beautiful sunny day.
The sky vibrant blue and a soft breeze was tickling Bubu's whiskers.

Ruth was about to bake one of her famous raspberry sponge cakes.

She suggested Papi and Bubu might enjoy a nice jaunt out the back field.

The vast field of tall grass turned into a forest with a small stream curving along through it, very refreshing to paddle in on a hot day.

Papi agreed it sounded like a nice idea, he could bring out his fly net and do some insect hunting while Bubu could have a run about.

Off they went, Papi with his fly net, wearing a sun hat followed by the pup at his heels loaded with the happy excitement of adventure.

They went through the cottage garden filled with flowers of all colours and scents, past a greenhouse delivering a whiff of ripe luscious tomatoes right up Bubu's excitable nostrils.

Bubu couldn't help but lick his lips and smush his nose into every available smell they walked past.

Finally wiggling down a little overgrown path, dodging some stinging nettles and coming out into the large open field of long grass fluttering in the wind.

"Stay close little fellow, let's go find the stream for you to have a splash in."
Bubu trundled along behind Papi. Catching the flattened grass patches he made with each footstep before the grass floated back up into place.

Something caught the pup's attention.
"Ooh" thought Bubu "Is that another dog?..a new friend?!"
He galavanted at high speed bulldozing through the long grass straight over to his new friend.

A wide eyed deer
stared at him,
frozen undecided
whether to run or
hide from the
strange looking
creature who
appeared out of
nowhere.

"Hello" said Bubu
"What kind of dog are
you?"
"You have really long
legs."

Bambi blinked.
"I'm, a deer, what's, a
dog?"

The deer was now
intrigued and sensed no
danger from the odd
little creature.

"I'm a dog!" Exclaimed the pup.

"Hello dog, I'm Bambi". Said the soft fawn coloured deer.

"My name is Bubu, I'm walking with Grandpa Papi". Just then Bubu turned to point out Papi and realised with a fright that he could no longer see him, just a lot of long grass swaying in the breeze.

"Oh no, where's my human!"
"We were going to the forest stream."
"I'm lost!" gasped Bubu.

"I know the forest stream." Reassured the deer, looking down at Bubu with his large gentle eyes.
"I live in the forest, I can take you there, Bubu dog."

"You live in a forest? How exciting!" Barked Bubu.

"Follow me" Bambi said and elegantly pounced through the sea of grass.

Bubu followed attempting his own
version of the Bambi bounce.

He quite enjoyed it.

The bouncing duo chatted joyfully sharing and comparing their versions of life.

House living, and forest living sounding so different in most ways imaginable.

Bubu thought to himself, as much as sleeping under the stars must be beautiful, he rather liked his comfy cushion bed and snuggle blanket.

The field met the forest, the stream trickling peacefully along in front of them.

Bubu could see Papi off in the distance, he was calling.
"Bubuuuu where are you little fellow, here boy."

"I'll leave you to go to Papi, he's calling you."
Said Bambi.
"I'm glad we met Bubu dog. Enjoy the rest of your day."

"Thank you Bambi, I'll try to visit again. Bye."

The pup bounced happily over to
greet Papi with nose bumps and
bum wiggles.

"Bubu! Little fellow, I've been looking for
you, who's a good boy!"

"Let's go dip our toes in the river before
you have to go home for your dinner".

Just like that Bubu's mini adventure came
to a happy conclusion as he splashed around
in the cool stream.

He went home that day covered in mud
happy and sleepy.

His humans never understood
what started his craze for
bouncing, but they praised him
infinitely for all his lovely jumping
displays.

Lightning Source UK Ltd.
Milton Keynes UK
UKHW050841090223
416624UK00004B/487